The
Great Detective

Radar Scope photograph of New York City, taken from a B-17 by Radiation Laboratory staff members. This photograph was taken with high definition apparatus which provides radar identification of important military objectives. The outline of Manhattan Island clearly shows the Hudson river with its shipping docks. The Metropolitan Museum can be seen jutting out into Central Park. On the New Jersey side the Hackensack river is clearly visible. At the time the photograph was taken the plane was directly over the spot in the center of the circle. Distance is indicated by the concentric circles used for navigation and bombing.

The
Great Detective

by

Wesley W. Stout

Chrysler Corporation
Detroit, Michigan
1946

An investor has a natural interest in how well his savings have been put to work by the managers of a corporation in which he has invested.

Here is a report of another kind: of how the investor's money, plus his taxes, was put to work in the defense of his country in a time of great peril.

This book deals with only one such instance of many within Chrysler Corporation, one of many thousands in American industry generally, but there were few more dramatic or more decisive.

Foreword

In radar the Allies were engaged in a deadly race with the enemy for technical supremacy from the first year of the war, a race in which they continuously and increasingly bested German science and manufacture for all Germany's acknowledged prowess in these fields.

"We fell behind technically," said Grand Admiral Doenitz, when captured. "We were unable to build short wave radar to compete with the Anglo-American improved radio location equipment."

Dr. DuBridge, Director of the Radiation Laboratory, has written generously of Chrysler's part in short wave radar. If he and his fellow physicists found it worth while to work with our engineers and production men, we found it exciting to work with these magicians of electronics. Working as a team on radar and other strange new weapons, American Science and American Industry discovered a mutual respect which, if it is carried over into peace, will not have been the least gain of the war.

K. T. KELLER
President

Chrysler Engineering Division building where a fundamental problem of gun-laying radar was solved. (below) the Dodge Main plant where the SCR-584 radar mount was made.

The Great Detective

When the Japs struck Pearl Harbor on that Sunday morning of December, 1941, the public was told that a detecting device had flushed their carrier-based planes when these still were half an hour away. This was radar, though the name was not spoken then or until long after.

The public was puzzled. It was familiar with the nest of horns of the old sound-listening post, photographs of which it had seen often. But as any high school boy knows, sound travels only 700 miles an hour, little faster than a 1946 jet plane, and dissipates so quickly that it is lost within a few miles.

What was this legerdemain, then? The public learned for the first time on April 24, 1943, through a guarded Army-Navy joint press release. Censorship was restored after this fragmentary mention and not lifted again until Japan had sued for peace.

Radar is a Navy-coined word for radio detection and range finding.

It was radar which enabled the RAF to break the back of the German air blitz of England in 1940, thereby stopping Hitler from invading the island.

It was radar which took most of the sting out of the V-1 buzz bomb.

1

Herman L. Weckler
Vice President and General Manager of Chrysler Corporation

K. T. Keller
President of Chrysler Corporation

It was radar which defeated the German's new U-boat technic.

It was radar, more than any other one factor, which disrupted Jap shipping and destroyed the Jap Navy.

It was radar which made possible the accurate bombing of Germany through the nearly constant winter overcast.

It was the intervention of microwave radar, specifically the SCR-584 set for which Chrysler made the fundamental component, which saved the day for us at the Anzio beachhead.

It was the SCR-584, again, which drove the Luftwaffe away from the Normandy beachheads.

It was radar which won the war, according to Sir Stafford Cripps, who was chairman of the British

2

F. W. Slack
in charge Radar
work at Chrysler
Engineering

F. J. Lamborn
Vice President and
General Manager,
Dodge Division

C. W. Hirsch
Superintendent
Radar Division at
Dodge

Radio Board during the most critical period. "If radar had not prevented the enemy from getting by surprise over England," he said, after the war had ended, "I don't know where we would have been. It played a greater part in the war's outcome than did the atomic bomb itself. It contributed to the winning of the war more than any other single factor."

Beginning as a purely defensive weapon, radar changed the face of war more than any single development since the airplane, for one of war's great weapons is surprise, and it defeated most tactical concealment. Yet it had become by 1944 a superlative weapon of offense.

More was spent on radar by the United States Government than on the atomic bomb. Up to July, 1945, $2,700,000,000 of radar equipment had been delivered to the Army and Navy.

Long before radar was named publicly in 1943,

Chrysler Corporation had been asked by the Radiation Laboratory of the National Defense Research Committee and by the Army to design the antenna mount, a then unsolved basic element of a revolutionary short-wave radar set, and to manufacture it in secret. The design of the instrument was assigned to the Company's Engineering Division, and the Dodge Division was told to prepare to manufacture it. By early 1944, Dodge had turned out 2,092 of these mysterious mechanisms.

War means haste and Chrysler was required to make its price estimate without an opportunity of breaking down the instrument into its component parts, studying each detail, as would be done in normal manufacturing. As the mount had yet to be designed, this was impossible.

At the request of the War Department, the Corporation submitted an estimate of $16,451 apiece, pleasantly surprising the Radiation Laboratory, the Signal Corps and the General Electric Company, the prime contractor, who had, they said, expected any figure up to $50,000. Yet on a cost and fee contract such as often has been misunderstood as neither rewarding economies nor penalizing waste, Chrysler's actual price to the Government was $9,386 each, a saving to the taxpayer of nearly $15,000,000 or approximately 43% of the estimated cost.

The antenna mount made by Chrysler sends out 2,000 microwave (10 centimeters) radio pulses a second, each pulse traveling at the speed of light and

Signal Corps officer attaching the plastic-enclosed radar antenna to the spinner motor.

Recording van on right made records of radar opera-
tions for the study of anti-aircraft research groups.

beamed as a searchlight is focused. This radio beam searches the sky and whenever it intercepts any object, such as an airplane or a ship, it bounces or echoes back from it into the antenna.

Such is the uncanny cunning of the radar unit that from this faint sigh it computes instantly and automatically the direction, distance, speed, altitude and course of the object. An auxiliary instrument distinguishes the object automatically as friend or foe. If the latter, the radar fastens its electronic teeth into the target and follows it thenceforth, however the plane may twist or dodge, with the tenacity of a bulldog.

There are many types of radar, large and small.

That for which Chrysler designed and manufactured the antenna mount is the anti-aircraft set known as the SCR-584, the most complex mobile weapon known to modern war. It was the standard radar issued for each heavy anti-aircraft gun battery, housed in a 10-ton semi-trailer. Each battery consisted of four 90mm guns, an IFF (identification, friend or foe) unit; a power plant; an M-9 gun director or computer which is a robot brain; and the scanning pedestal made by Chrysler upon the minute accuracy of which the performance of the entire battery depends.

This antenna mount is a large and intricately geared, wired and motored mechanism crowned by what looks like a big colander or sieve, familiarly called the "dish" by the G.I. Six feet in diameter, it contains 6,440 equal holes, meaningless as far as the function of the instrument goes. In its center is a plastic enclosed and exquisitely accurate antenna rotated by a motor at 1,750 revolutions a minute.

From this antenna are beamed into the heavens short wave radio pulses one-millionth of a second in duration at intervals of only one two-thousandth of a second. A modulator stores up power and shoots it out in bursts ten times more powerful than the strongest American commercial radio station uses. A cavity magnetron, a million times more powerful than any previous magnetron, oscillates violently 3,000 times in that one-millionth of a second, or at the incredible rate of three billion times a second.

*Front cutaway view of the complete
radar mechanism as Chrysler built it.*

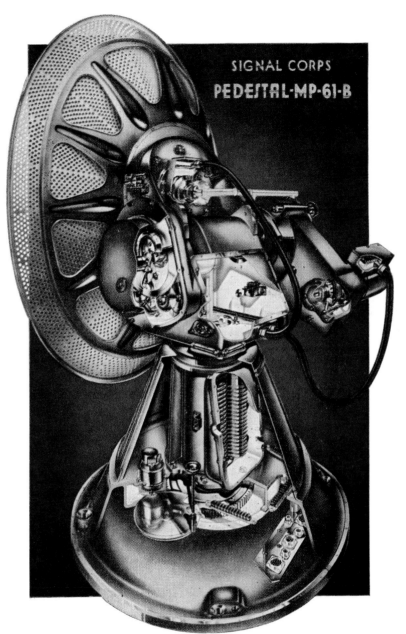

SIGNAL CORPS
PEDESTAL-MP-61-B

Rear cutaway view of the complete radar mechanism as Chrysler built it.

9

Traveling with the speed of light, this echo will return to the radar antenna in a hundred one-millionths of a second from a plane ten miles away. Within one one-millionth of a second after the transmitter has completed its signal, the receiver connected to the same antenna must be at full sensitivity in order that it respond to the faint energy of the returning echo.

A special vacuum tube devised for the SCR-584 radar performs this all but instantaneous switch, repeating it a thousand times a second. Since the outgoing burst is a powerful blast, its power must be kept out of the ultra-sensitive receiver where it would destroy the tubes and circuits set up to catch and

Chrysler radar teamed with 90-mm battery at Camp Davis, North Carolina, Army anti-aircraft proving ground.

amplify the weak echo. The tube insures this by providing a short-circuit path for the transmitter's power, a tiny gap between two needle-like copper conductors that are enclosed in an atmosphere of gas of controlled pressure. An excellent insulator, this gap will stop the flow of current of ordinary voltage, but the high voltage of the transmitter leaps the gap and so by-passes the receiver. When the echo returns a few millionths of a second later, its feeble few millionths of a watt current is blocked away from the transmitter by the gap and so passes undissipated into the receiver.

A very small fraction of the energy beamed out by the antenna reaches the target. As most of this glances off the target haphazardly and is lost in space, a still tinier fraction of that power echoes back to be amplified by the receiver just as your radio amplifies what it hears, but to an infinitely greater degree. If you can conceive of a million times a million, that is the amplification produced by the SCR-584's receiver tubes.

In commercial radio an electronic tube takes the broadcast from the antenna, rectifies it, changes its frequency to one that is audible to the human ear and transmits it to an amplifier. Even though electrons may travel across such a tube at speeds up to three million feet a second, it would be far too slow for the billion-cycle frequencies of microwave radar. A special detector had to be contrived for the

SCR-584, a tiny silicon crystal and a cat-whisker probe of fine tungsten wire in a porcelain cartridge. Entering the receiver, the radar echo impresses its minute voltage on the crystal causing electrons to flow from the crystal to the cat-whisker probe instantly.

The great dish, officially known as a paraboloid because of its parabolic contour, and driven by two gear trains, swings laterally around the horizon (azimuth) and up and down the heavens (elevation) as it scans or probes. Radar waves behave much as light waves do except that the microwave penetrates the densest fog or storm front. The parabolic surface of the dish focuses the radar beam just as a searchlight reflector focuses light waves.

Your radio news and entertainment is reflected from the outer atmosphere and so follows the curve of the earth indefinitely. But like television, all radar sets can see only in a straight line. If the view is not obstructed by mountains, buildings or other physical objects, the SCR-584 radar will pick up a plane at a distance of 45 miles. Other radars function up to 200 miles, depending upon the elevation of the set and the elevation of the target, but lack the accuracy necessary to directing gun fire.

As the antenna mount rotates, a cathode ray tube operating on the principle of television and known as the PPI or Plan Position Indicator translates the returning echoes into a visual map for the radar

Chrysler-built radar directing strategic aircraft in "close support" at Eupen, Belgium—November, 1944.

crew. When the scope watcher begins his vigil he spends his first ten minutes in studying the ground images, such as hills, which appear on the glass, to familiarize himself with the normal—what he should see. If the same images show up in the same positions on each sweep of the antenna they may be presumed to be fixed objects.

But when a strange blob of light appears it is suspected of being an intruder, and if it changes position with each sweep of the antenna the scope operator reports an unidentified aircraft echo to his fellow, the IFF operator and to the nearest anti-aircraft operations room, giving the range and bearing of the object, these being visible on the graduated glass. The blobs of light, unlike televised images, are not photographic, but they are easily interpretable to a trained man, and the scope is specially treated to hold its images for 20 to 25 seconds on each sweep.

If the plane continues to approach, the interrupted beam echoing back into the antenna becomes stronger and stronger. By the time the plane has come within 20 miles both the IFF unit and the operations room will have identified it as friend or foe. The operations room can report only whether friendly aircraft are in the vicinity, but the IFF, a British development, answers the $64 question surely.

Its coded signal is returned auto-

Camouflaged radar trap for enemy planes set up alongside a graveyard in Italian hills. 90-mm batteries are nearby.

Heavily camouflaged radars set up across the river from Cologne as we battled for the Rhine in late winter of 1945.

matically from the plane if it is one of our own, returned without the knowledge or aid of the plane crew. There is no response from an enemy plane. Every American and British plane or vessel carried a small auxiliary radio set, the sole purpose of which was to answer this challenge. Each set contained an explosive charge and a detonator. Pilots were under order to destroy it in any emergency involving capture. In the event of a crack-up severe enough to knock out the crew, the force of the landing was counted upon to explode the charge.

If the IFF gets no response, indicating a hostile plane, one member of the radar crew now locks the antenna mount on this specific target. From then on the mount ceases to search and points unerringly at the target, however it may maneuver. The battery will have been alerted on first contact. The position of the mount is transmitted automatically by self-synchronous generators to the gun-director. This robot brain of 160 tubes, most of them not unlike the vacuum tubes in your home radio sets, precisely predicts where the plane will be at the instant the 90mm shells will arrive, often as much as 20 seconds later. This position is transmitted again by self-synchronous generators to the guns, the muzzles of which are swung by remote control power drives. From radar to gun, approximately 500 vacuum tubes are at work, and not a single human hand except for that of the range operator who locks the radar mount on this one target.

The pilot may climb into the stratosphere or drop to 50 feet, he may duck into a cloudbank, he may swing 90 degrees to right or left; as long as he does not retreat out of radar range the microwave beam will follow and hold him inexorably. Clear or stormy, night or day, high or low, there is no place to hide from this electronic feeler except at a harmless distance.

The order to begin firing is given, the fuses are cut and the flak storm of 80 rounds a minute meets the plane. The pilot's only hope is to play hide-and-seek with the flak by what the Air Force calls "evasive tactics" and you would call broken field running.

The microwave beam is so powerful that it can "see" the shells traveling through space. When one

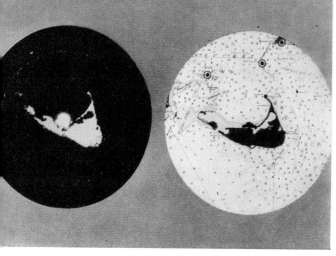

Nantucket on aerial radar scope (left) and actual chart of the island. Land appears white, water black, on radar screen.

Courtesy "Army Ordnance" Magazine

bursts, the reflection on the scope shows a characteristic increase and the operator knows whether the shells are exploding short of, beyond or on the target.

During the hours of quiet between attacks, the SCR-584 is a watchdog standing 24-hour sentry duty, the antenna mount never ceasing to rotate as the beam probes the skies.

Though the Corporation ceased in 1944 to manufacture radar mounts, the Engineering division, under a separate development contract with the Radiation Laboratory, located at Massachusetts Institute of Technology, perfected a spiral scanning mechanism using even shorter waves to replace the antenna in the original SCR-584, which was the bulk of Dodge's production.

During the war, each side jammed or blocked the other's radar at times, and the longer the wave length the more vulnerable it was to jamming. Though the Nazis never effectively jammed the

SCR-584, the Signal Corps and the Radiation Laboratory knew that it could be jammed and so the latter asked Chrysler Engineering to go to an ultra short wave and spiral scanning pattern, jam-proof in their professional judgment.

Just as the Dodge radar shop was concluding manufacture in April, 1944, the first performance reports reached the Corporation. Dr. I. A. Getting of the Radiation Laboratory wrote Mr. Keller April 4, 1944:

"It was not until the last month or so that any SCR-584 arrived in the active theaters of war. They are now in use on the major battle-fronts . . . Recent experiences in landing in Sicily and Italy have shown the absolute necessity of adequate anti-aircraft protection. When such protection was absent, destruction of men and supplies by enemy airplanes was extreme. This emphasis on anti-aircraft fire and the usefulness of the SCR-584 already has created a shortage of this equipment within the Army.

"There is very recent evidence from combat experience in England and Italy that the enemy is attempting to counteract the effectiveness of the SCR-584 with jamming methods. Last year, at the request of General Colton, the Radiation Laboratory undertook the responsibility for anti-jamming developments. This program now has been given very high priority. One part of it requires the modification by field kits of the SCR-584 to shorter wave lengths. A necessary part of this modification is a spiral scan mechanism. Your Engineering division has been very cooperative and has succeeded in developing a mechanism which we are confident will satisfy our needs."

Dr. Getting had the Anzio beachhead in mind, in particular. The first SCR-584's to leave this country in 1943 were sent to North Africa for crew instruction. The German-Italian air forces had jammed the 268 radar, the predecessor of the SCR-584, and were bombing the Anzio beachhead and harbor shipping indiscriminately by night, an area so congested that any bomb dropped was almost certain to hit men or equipment.

The enemy artillery in the surrounding hills had every foot of the beach and harbor indexed and bomber raids always were timed with intense artillery fire. To turn on a search-light was an invitation to annihilation; even flash-lights or the lighting of a cigarette were banned. It was touch and go whether we should be thrown back into the sea.

The first two SCR-584's rushed from Naples were landed at Anzio from an LST February 24, 1944, and the trailers quickly buried up to their roofs in outsized fox holes. The second night a formation of twelve Nazi bombers came cruising over unsuspectingly. Four 90mm guns directed by these two radars shot down seven of the twelve in flames, though the radar crews were unfamiliar with their new equipment. A 58% loss is even more decisive than it sounds, for the surviving 42% will be driven into saving themselves rather than harassing you.

The Germans never again came over Anzio in formation and almost a week passed before a single plane returned to test out the defenses. It, too, was shot down. "Without doubt, they (the twelve SCR-584's then on the beachhead) are largely responsible for the successful anti-aircraft defense of Anzio," said an official report.

More direct news of the prowess of the SCR-584 reached the Corporation in August, 1944, after the invasion of France, through the courtesy of the Chief of Staff, General George Marshall, who forwarded a then secret letter addressed to him by General Sir Frederick A. Pile, commanding the British defense against the buzz bombs.

"I am writing to thank you for the great assistance

Blind-flying dive bombers, fighters and photographic planes were directed by radar from this SCR-584 trailer.

you have given us in meeting the flying bombs," the letter read. "The equipment you have sent us is absolutely first-class, and every day we are getting better results with it. We are employing the SCR-584 with the new predictor. This predictor also is an outstanding job. Finally, there is a fuse so secret that I can describe it only by its nickname in this country, "Bonzo."

"With this fuse we have cut down the number of rounds fired per flying bomb destroyed to well under 100, and the best of batteries actually are getting one bomb to every 40 rounds. Our percentage of kills is not yet high enough, but it is going up at a very nice pace and we are already far ahead of the fighter planes. . . . General Eisenhower has lent me twenty of your batteries and they are now in action on the coast. They are a grand lot of chaps and have shot down large numbers of flying bombs."

If the percentage of kills was not then high enough to suit General Sir Frederick, it quickly became so. On a later Sunday in August, 101 V-1 buzz bombs were detected approaching the coast of England. Of these only four got past the SCR-584 radar-directed defense.

"Bonzo," the very secret fuse, was the radio proximity fuse, also an American invention, from which the veil of censorship was not lifted until the Fall of 1945. Smaller than a pint milk bottle, the VT fuse contained five radio tubes, each about a third the size of a cigarette. Instead of being timed to explode

*Radar-making machine tools begin to arrive at the Dodge
Plant. These are radial drills in their shipping wrappers.*

at a pre-determined point, a shell equipped with a
VT fuse was set off by radio waves when it came
within 70 feet of an enemy bomber. Another type of
VT fuse used in howitzer fire was exploded by radio
impulses reflected from the ground instead of from a
flying target. Even men in foxholes could not escape
their deadly fragmentation at about tree-top height.

Radar even enabled the British and our Air Force
to backtrack the buzz bombs to their sources in

23

France, Belgium and Holland, then to bomb these launching installations. On D-Day, June 6th, 1944, though the French coast was heavily overcast, the German coastal defenses showed up plainly on the scopes of airborne radar sets and enabled Allied bombers to lay down a bomb barrage which paralyzed many of the Nazi defenses for a time. Every bomb dropped was directed by radar and none hit an Allied soldier though the German and our lines often were as close together as a "quarter past three," in artilleryman's language.

Thirty-nine SCR-584 sets were landed on Normandy beaches on D-Day and were so deadly in their effect that the Germans soon pulled their aircraft out except for sporadic sorties.

On the last night of the German evacuation of Boulogne, heavy guns on the Dover coast sank eleven ships out of eighteen at a range of twenty miles, ships which only radar could see.

Air Marshal Tedder, Air Chief of the North African campaign, credited radar above tanks with the rout of Rommel. "Radar," he said after the war ended, "caught Rommel's fuel ships just outside Tobruk before the battle of El Alamein. Later it enabled us to strangle his Mediterranean supply line, and this led to the collapse of his armies."

* * * * *

In the course of the development of the microwave SCR-584 gun-laying radar, the Radiation Laboratory found itself faced with new mechanical problems in the vital antenna mount. While the principle was the same used in earlier radars, a much greater mechanical accuracy was demanded, and as the SCR-584 must be easily moved from place to place, there were limits of size and weight. Accuracy would depend entirely upon the gearing, size and weight would depend principally upon the gearing. A lesser weight factor was the antenna dish or paraboloid. An experimental paraboloid had been made of spun and cast aluminum, no longer to be had.

In late April of 1942, Dr. Karl T. Compton, President of Massachusetts Institute of Technology, seat of the Radiation Laboratory, phoned his friend, Mr. Keller, to ask if two Laboratory men could come to

Gears held to exquisite accuracies were cut on the gear shapers and shavers shown here.

Tool men at work. Chrysler brought in extra ones to help engineer the tooling of the radar job.

Detroit to talk with him about their paraboloid problem. Dr. L. A. DuBridge, Director of the Laboratory, and his aide, Dr. I. A. Getting, arrived the next day.

After studying the drawings they brought with them, Mr. Keller said he thought Chrysler could handle the paraboloid, stamping it out of steel at the Dodge plant. Unfamiliar with the art of forming thin sections of steel in presses, Drs. DuBridge and Getting questioned whether the necessary accuracy could be had by this method. In principle, they explained, the dish focused the radio beam as a battleship searchlight reflector focuses a million candlepower light. Mr. Keller satisfied them, however, that the piece could be made to close accuracy on automobile body presses.

They did not speak of gearing, but it so happened that Chrysler Corporation was making radar antenna mount gears for Research Enterprise, Ltd., Canadian makers of radar, and so knew something of the gearing problems involved. Chrysler merely made the gears to the specifications of the Canadian company, but Chrysler men never had ceased to wonder why it should be necessary to use so many gears to accomplish the reductions necessary in such a mechanism.

For all they could see, the required antenna mount gear reductions could be attained much more compactly and with greater accuracy in operation if an entirely different type of gearing were used. It seemed to them that many gears must compound the possibilities of error in operation, while if the same reductions could be realized with fewer gears, the instrument must become more accurate, to say nothing of being lighter, less bulky and easier to make. Mr. Keller mentioned this to his visitors.

They then disclosed that they were troubled by just this problem in the SCR-584 mount and discussed gearing methods at length with Keller. The tentative solution he proposed led them, as soon as they had returned to Cambridge, to recommend to the Army that Chrysler be employed to design and build in its entirety the microwave radar antenna mount of which the paraboloid is one detail.

In essence, what Chrysler was asked to do was to work out the unsolved mechanical problems of short-wave gun-laying radar and, having done so, to manufacture the design in quantities.

The significance of this assignment lay in the fact that the antenna mount is the eyes of radar. The gun-director and the guns can act only on what it reports and no more accurately than it reports. Or in the words of the Signal Corps, the mount was an "unsolved detail and a most difficult engineering and manufacturing problem; it must be extremely accurate, for on its accuracy depends the accuracy of the computer and the fire of the guns."

The SCR-584 had been methodically planned to cope with the planes of the future—speeds up to 600-700 miles an hour and altitudes up to 60,000 feet. Such speeds demanded the long-range destruction of a hostile plane, at a distance from the radar set of not less than 8 miles, and its discovery at a greater distance than aircraft can be seen by the eye on the clearest day. Hence the need of a new short wave technic and the ultra accuracy asked of the mechanism in order to harness the short wave's precision to the guns.

An error of only a few seconds of a degree in an instrument becomes an error of many yards when the line of sight is carried out to 10,000 feet and beyond, the error increasing with the distance. What had been a tolerable error in anti-aircraft fire when the ceiling

Stamping out on an automobile fender press the radar "dish" which focuses radio beams as a searchlight reflector focuses light rays.

29

of service planes commonly was 12,000 feet and their speed around 150 miles an hour became intolerable against better planes. The radio echo makes no errors, but the least backlash in the gears would mistranslate the echo's report, so to hit a plane flying in the stratosphere at speeds approaching that of sound called for something approaching perfection in the gears which tell the guns where to aim.

George Slider and L. P. Smith of Chrysler Engineering were sent to Cambridge April 29, 1942, to see what had been done up to then. The Radiation Laboratory people showed them the layout drawings and a wooden model of an experimental antenna mount which had been made by a neighboring Massachusetts factory and was then on test at Camp Davis.

All agreed that it was impractical for use or manufacture. It was too heavy and cumbersome; it had not been designed for production; two long trains of spur gears, with no interchangeability of parts, defeated close accuracy. The Army was talking about 3,000 units and the manufacturers were not equipped to build even a hundred.

Slider and Smith were asked to stay over and meet General Colton, director of the Signal Corps' Radio Reflection division, the next day, May first. General Colton felt that the antenna mount should be redesigned from scratch, explained the Army's urgent need of thousands of SCR-584 radar sets for antiaircraft gun-laying, and its concern about this "un-

solved detail and most difficult engineering and manufacturing problem."

Manufacture must begin by the following April.
This meant that all tools must be on order by Labor
Day and installed by February. All the tooling would

*The short wave beam makes no errors, but radar is no
more accurate than its gears, here being machined.*

be hard to find, the most critical a group of special
boring mills built to order. Tool makers in normal
times ask three months for the design of such a
machine tool.

In other words, the Army was asking Chrysler to
solve a difficult unsolved mechanical problem and

then to manufacture within eleven months and against all the extraordinary obstacles incident to war, a complex mechanism not even defined on paper as yet.

The Chrysler engineers returned via Schenectady, New York, where, at the General Electric plant, they were joined the next morning by H. L. Weckler, Vice President and General Manager of Chrysler Corporation; Fred Lamborn, Vice President and General Manager of the Dodge division; and Fred Slack of the Corporation's Engineering division. General Electric had been commissioned to make some of the electronic elements of the SCR-584 and to assemble, test and make final delivery of the complete radar unit to the Signal Corps.

The Chrysler group were back in Detroit Sunday morning with the design already roughed out. They were hardly at their desks Monday morning when the Signal Corps issued a letter of intent to the Corporation for the design of the mount and the semi-trailer to house it; and General Colton was phoning Mr. Keller to express the Army's hope that Chrysler could begin work at once on what then was described only as "a highly confidential development."

Chrysler's achievements in radar were basically two; first, the design, an original piece of engineering

Clear or stormy, night or day, high or low, there is no place in the skies to hide from the SCR-584 radar.

posing many problems without known parallel applications, and therefore requiring creative solutions. Of these creative solutions, the most important was the devising of an unique method of gearing.

Most readers know what a gear is, usually a toothed wheel, called a "spur" gear, which meshes or mates with another toothed wheel. Reduction is a primary purpose of gears, and simple enough. Suppose your car motor turns over 3,600 times a minute. Obviously, your car wheels can not revolve at this speed. In order to harness the motor's power to the wheels, the former's revolutions are stepped down by means of gears to the drive shaft which, in turn, is geared into the rear axle.

Little gears meshing into bigger gears accomplish this stepping-down. For example, a small gear meshing into one four times its diameter necessarily must revolve four times while the larger one turns once.

Assembly of the unlubricated spinner motor which rotates at the rate of 1,750 times a minute.

In an automobile and in most geared machinery the reduction problem is a simple one best achieved with conventional spur gears. But when the reduction is, say, more than 1,000 to 1, as in the SCR-584 radar mount, this method would call for a long and bulky train of gears beyond the weight and size limitations fixed by the Signal Corps for a mobile radar, and too inaccurate for the direction of guns.

A gear is round. Any full circle, whether the earth's equator or the circumference of a dime, is divisible into 360 degrees of measurement; and since a degree contains 60 minutes, a circle of any size has 21,600 minutes of measurement.

The permissible accumulated error or backlash of the gear train of the antenna mount was fixed by the Signal Corps at 3.375 minutes (1 angular mil). This means that if ten gears were used to accomplish the required reduction, the average error must not exceed 3/10ths of a minute—and 3/10ths of a minute means 1/64,800th part of the gear's circumference. Ten gears then were too many for such accuracy, quite apart from their weight and bulk, and no fewer number of spur gears could produce the reduction called for.

The Signal Corps specified a motor turning 3,600 times a minute. A slow moving motor would have erased the reduction problem, but slow motors happen to be big and heavy, ruling them out. For the paraboloid dish to do its job of scanning the skies properly, its drive shaft should not turn more than 8 times a minute in azimuth (horizontally) and less than 4 times a minute in elevation (up and down). To step 3,600 down to 8 and to 4 called for reductions of 472 to 1 and 1080 to 1 respectively.

Chrysler engineers did this within a very small space by inventing a method of gearing never before used in any mechanism, so far as they know.

At first glance, this gear train appears to be a simple planetary train, known to any engineer. Such a train has three sections. The central member is a sun gear. The second member is made up of planet gears, usually three, revolving around the sun gear and driven by it. The planets mesh in turn with and revolve inside of a larger gear, with teeth cut inside, the third member and called the annulus.

Such a gear train is a commonplace of engineering, though not widely used. As any of the three members can be made the input gear, any one made the output, this train may be used as an overdrive, underdrive or reverse. But as its limit of reduction normally is three and a half to one, simple planetary gearing could not scratch the surface of a reduction of more than 1,000 to 1, and so would have been disregarded by most engineers.

Chrysler designed a train beginning with the same three members, a sun gear driven by the motor at the motor's speed; three planets in a carrier or spider to which all the planet shafts are attached and which

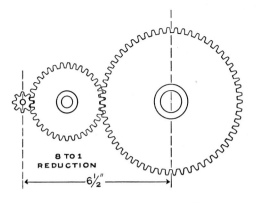

8 TO 1 REDUCTION

6½"

Using conventional spur gears, shown above,
6½ inches are required for an 8 to 1 reduction.

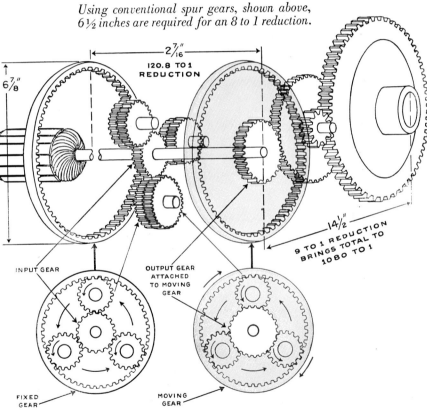

2 7/16"

120.8 TO 1 REDUCTION

6 7/8"

14½"

9 TO 1 REDUCTION
BRINGS TOTAL TO
1080 TO 1

INPUT GEAR

OUTPUT GEAR
ATTACHED
TO MOVING
GEAR

FIXED
GEAR

MOVING
GEAR

Chrysler accomplished a 1080 to 1 reduction, as shown above,
by using a special planetary type gear arrangement 2 7/16
inches thick and 6 7/8 inches in diameter to achieve a reduc-
tion of 120.8 to 1 and then having this in turn connect with
three conventional spur gears with an additional reduction
of almost 9 to 1. Thus, the entire reduction from driving center
to output center was achieved in a space of 14½ inches.

Inspector gauging the large 14½-inch gears which move the radar "dish" as it scans the heavens.

forces them to move together instead of individually; and the larger gear inside which they turn.

The planets turn both on their own axes and in the much wider circle of the outside gear. Therefore, the spider must be moving more slowly than the sun gear. This plus the difference between the 17 teeth of the sun gear and the 19 teeth of the planets creates a reduction, but one of only two and a half to one in all.

By "imagineering", Chrysler engineers increased this reduction to 121 to 1 within almost the same space. They did it by means of two added steps. First, they made the planet gears compound. That is to say, two gears were cut, one above the other, on each blank. Adapting an old but largely forgotten principle, sometimes spoken of as the "odd tooth", they gave the upper planets 19 teeth, the lower only 18. Only the upper mesh with the sun gear and the third member.

Now they added a fourth member, a second annulus gear a little smaller than its mate—54 teeth instead of 55. The lower planet teeth mesh into this fourth gear and turn inside it. The motor's power is transmitted by the sun gear through the planets to the third member, the normal annulus gear. But this gear can't turn, being clamped to a base. As it can't move, it becomes a fulcrum, passing the power on by leverage through the lower planets to the lower, movable, annulus or output gear.

The reduction which began faintly in the simple planetary train is compounded to 121 to 1 by the one

The pedestal starts down the machine line. Boring, drilling and milling machines in the foreground.

tooth difference between the upper and lower planets. The greatest reduction is had by the least differential in teeth, and the least differential is one tooth obviously. With each complete revolution of the planets inside the fixed annulus, the output annulus moves only the distance of one of its 54 teeth.

Exactly how this works can be explained only trigonometrically, meaning that it is a compound process of a complexity which defies simplification. Yet the actual gear train is beautifully clean and simple in its lines. It looks so easy to the eye, but the layman who tries to trace the evaporation of 121 to 1 between the entrance and exit of the power, finds the train as exasperating as a tough mechanical puzzle.

Its deceptive innocence can be illustrated this way: The sun gear lifts easily out of the planets, is easily put back. The upper annulus lifts easily out of mesh with the planets, is replaced as easily. The planets in their spider lift easily out of the lower annulus—but try to replace them! Unless you know the formula, trying to put these back into mesh is as futile as trying to solve the combination lock of a vault at random, and for the same reason. Unless he has memorized the location points, even an engineer can not rejoin these two members.

Complex as it is in formula, it is simplicity itself and troubleproof in service. Compound planet gears, though rare, are not new. What is unique in the design to the best of Chrysler's belief, is the combination of dual planet gears with a fourth member, a second annulus gear.

Having created a reduction of 121 to 1 between the input and the output gears, the rest is easy: 1080 being only about nine times 121, spur gearing in two steps gives this final reduction in elevation; 472 being only about four times 121, this final reduction in azimuth is accomplished by spur gears in one step.

By means of the same new gearing principle,

Chrysler Engineering later was to take approximately a ton of weight out of the gear boxes of the huge T-92 and T-93 mobile guns which it designed and built for Ordnance.

The Corporation's second contribution to the microwave radar program was an engineered production tool-up and process of manufacture whereby this complex instrument, including gears held to a precision beyond anything known in commercial manufacture, was made in quantities, quickly and economically—for the mount was a problem of manufacture even more than one of design. Accustomed to making gears to fine accuracy, Chrysler planned its production to accomplish the delicate limits required.

There are many more gears in the mount than those previously described. The returning radio echo gives the direction, speed, distance, altitude and course of a hostile plane. This information must be transmitted identically to the gun-director. Chrysler so designed the mount that this data is picked up directly from the main radar shafts, independently of the driving gears. By means of watch-like gears, the information is conveyed mechanically to seven selsyn or duplicating devices which pass it on electronically to the gun-director.

The selsyns can report the data no more accurately than it reaches them, so there can be no backlash whatever in the selsyn gears. Absolutely precise gears, however, would not function. The Chrysler solution was split gears, an ingenuity in which the tension of steel springs set inside the two halves of a gear insure that it keeps its teeth lightly clamped to the teeth of its mating gear at all times. This is possible only when the loads involved are very light—flypower instead of horsepower, as an engineer would express it.

Another major problem was an unlubricated air seal on the spinner motor which revolves 1,750 times a minute. The air seal is necessary because moisture within the hollow radio frequency transmission lines would absorb the short wave impulses. The seal holds six pounds of pressure built up by a small compressor. Because oil or grease also would absorb radio frequencies, the seal could not be lubricated. Chrysler

The elevation housing machine line. Machine tools in the foreground are boring mills.

The radar "dish" oscillates up and down, right and left.
Here the elevation gear housing is being assembled.

had had experience with air seals on its fluid drive,
though not unlubricated. The answer was found in
Superfinish, a Chrysler development. Friction was
minimized by Superfinishing the bellows and seal to
95% optical flat surfaces, a microscopically smooth
finish. Even the carbon disc between the housing seal
and sleeve was Superfinished.

The heavy steel castings of the pedestal support
appeared to be just another set of castings of which
nothing but strength need be asked, yet the accuracy
of the paraboloid reflector and, ultimately, of the
guns, began with these innocent-looking pieces. Their

dimensions had to be exact, just as the accuracy of your watch begins with the precision of its backplate.

As Chrysler Engineering designing the wiring for quantity production, the mount was wired as it moved along the assembly line, with complete interchangeability, easy replaceability, and color coding of the wires for the easy distinguishing of one electrical circuit from another. The electrical industry usually cords its wires. Chrysler used the tape it had used in recent years on all car wiring, a synthetic, satisfying the Signal Corps that the tape would lose none of its qualities at 40 degrees below zero. It is self-quenching in case of fire from short circuits; it is impervious to moisture and to most acids, has a higher strength than the best rubber and an elasticity almost as good, while rubber of these characteristics would shatter at 40 below. The nearly automatic machines which wound the tape on radar wiring circuits are a Chrysler development.

When the Signal Corps in the Fall 1943 ordered the "tropicalization" of the radar wiring to protect it against fungus growths and insect damage, the Chrysler wiring already had been so treated, the same problem having arisen earlier on tanks and military trucks. The acids and strong alkalis commonly used in soldering are a contributing cause of the fungoid growths which attack insulation in regions of high humidity and temperature. Chrysler eliminated this accessory-before-the-fact by going to a special, mild, resin-based flux. An insecticide in the lacquer

*Bombers, fighters and photographic re-
connaissance planes could be directed to
their targets from ground radar plotting
rooms regardless of weather conditions.*

coating repels insects which, in the tropics, will eat virtually anything.

There is little but nylon, including human flesh, which fungus spores do not attack, though all pure cellulose acetates, of which nylon is one, resist fungi. Believe it or not, the spores ruin range-finders, gun telescopes, camera lenses and all other optical glass by etching the lens. The deadly enemy of wiring insulation is an Aspergillus species, a cousin of bread mold and so of the magic Penicillin, the spores of which in the tropics germinate in ordinary insulation much as onions do in a well-kept vegetable garden. This mold has the nasty habit of building up immunity to any given fungicide quickly; what kills it one season may be harmless the next.

Though Chrysler made the paraboloid reflector dish out of ordinary steel, it weighed no more than did the aluminum dish of the earliest Radiation Laboratory experimental model. The 6,640 half-inch holes in the dish saved 70 pounds—though weight was a secondary factor. The specifications required that the mount function smoothly in a 60-mile wind, not be overturned by a 100-mile hurricane. No 6-foot expanse of solid metal could oscillate long against such winds without something giving. Chrysler Engineering advanced perforation as the probable answer. The Radiation Laboratory agreed if the holes should be no larger than half an inch, beyond which they might allow some of the radio energy to leak through. Perforation was tested in Langley Field wind tunnels and proven; the holes reduced the air resistance sufficiently.

You take your radio antenna for granted—a few yards of almost any kind of wire will do. An anti-aircraft microwave radar antenna must concentrate its high energy in a narrow beam aimed more accurately than any gun; all the power must follow this beam, none leaking to one side or the other and, unlike any radio, the same antenna sends and receives. The RF lines, as the Army calls the concentric copper radio frequency transmission lines which pass through the whirling spinner motor transmitting and receiving the microwave impulses, had to be centered with extreme precision.

Elevation unit assembly line. The elevation gears swing the searching "dish" up and down the sky.

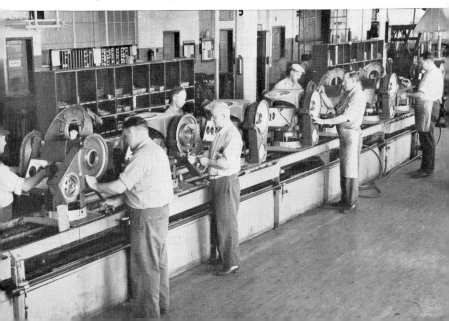

The front bearing on the spinner motor of one pilot model burnt out while it was under test at Camp Davis. Being outside the calculated microwave path, this motor is lubricated in contrast to the airseal previously described. Other front bearing failures followed. When the motors were torn down the bearings were found to be annealed by heat and the lubricating greases charred.

At first, this was supposed to be a mechanical failure. Dodge men could not believe this. The rear bearings never burned though the mechanical conditions were identical, nor did this failure occur in the front bearings in the roof tests at Dodge where motors were run for thousands of hours. A dozen different explanations were advanced, some blaming vibration.

Others, remembering the eccentricities of high frequency electricity when Chrysler had used a 13-megacycle current to bond brake lining to brake shoes, eliminating rivets, deduced that high frequency radiation leakage was cooking the bearings. This reasoning was supported by the fact that radio frequency current was not used in the roof tests where no bearing had burned, and by the odor of the charred lubricant, electric scorching having a smell all its own. This proved to be the answer. When Engineering phoned its findings to the Radiation Laboratory, the physicists there quickly designed a radio choke or trap which acted as a barrier to radiation leakage at this point, and there were no more bearing failures.

Pedestal support assembly line. The accuracy of the radar-directed guns begins with these heavy steel castings.

Master mechanics can not decide how best to make any part until they know just what that part is to be; they can not know what kinds and numbers of machine tools, fixtures and dies they need until they have settled upon how the parts are to be made. As fast as parts prints came from Engineering, tools were ordered, but design changes were frequent, as was inevitable with what really was a research problem, and changes of design usually changed the tooling.

The production sub-contract with General Electric was concluded September 22, 1942. It called for 2,750 units, the first ten production jobs to be delivered to Baltimore and Syracuse in April, 1943, rising to 50 mounts in May and levelling off at 400 a month in November. At this rate, the contract would have been completed by February of 1944, but further orders were to be expected.

Due to the changing course of the war, however, Dodge's schedule for the year was cut in February, 1943, from 2,500 units to 1,410, with a peak output of 200 monthly set for October and by the time October came the Signal Corps fixed its total requirements at only 1,470 units. To this were subsequently added 147 spare sets, 220 more unassigned SCR-584 units, 240 SP-1M units and 14 experimental A-70's. The latter was a modification of the SCR-584, intended for use with all coast defense guns for the detection of hostile warships, for which Chrysler Engineering had been given a development contract in 1943. The SP-1M was the Marine Corps' version of Navy radar SP.

Inspectors testing for backlash. Absolutely perfect gears would not function, but the error here must be extremely small.

Each elevating mechanism was given a three-hour test in especially equipped testing rooms.

In all, 2,098 SCR-584 radar units were made at a cost to the Government of about $20,000,000.

The first of the six tool room-made models of the antenna mount was delivered by Dodge to the Chrysler Engineering laboratories for life test December 4, 1942, the second shipped to General Electric the day after Christmas. Experimental models of an instrument of the newness and delicacy of microwave radar would, in normal times, be tested for a year, or even two, before fixing upon a production model, but this was war; production could not wait on methodical testing. Before the preliminary trials of the first two Dodge pilot models sent to the Anti-aircraft Board had been completed, Dodge had turned out 50 production mounts.

By the end of August, Dodge had shipped 610 units. About now, however, the General Staff came to a decision which soon resulted in a cancellation of the SCR-584 contract. This decision was that the air defense of continental United States no longer was necessary. The United Nations had won control of the air in all theaters and Axis planes were now too few and too preoccupied with defending their own to attempt even a token bombing of this country.

If the Axis ever had intended an attack in force on the East or West Coasts, or on the Great Lakes region by way of the polar air lanes, it had missed the boat. Radar watched more than the coasts; radar listening posts and anti-aircraft batteries were scattered

Women did most of the assembly of the slip rings and wiring of the main drive shaft.

through the Canadian bush into the Arctic Circle listening always for planes approaching on the Great Circle—planes that never came.

Therefore, on Columbus Day, 1943, the Signal Corps notified General Electric and its sub-contractors that it would no longer need large quantities of the SCR-584 and that the contract to make them would be terminated at the most economical point. This later was fixed at 1,470 sets, plus extras.

As a result of this changed schedule, Dodge delivered its 1,470th mount January 28, 1944, and between then and April 14th turned out the remainder in the form of spares, coast defense units and Marine Corps sets.

Laid out for a production of 24 mounts a day, the

radar shop had been held by the mutations of war to a maximum of 10 daily. The working force began to scatter in January to other war contracts, the last gone by mid-April. Before May, machines and tools were being moved out, a pilot line into storage in a Defense Plant Corporation warehouse in Indiana, most of the rest to other Chrysler war projects. New machinery was coming in for B-29 Superbomber engine pump parts. By July, the sixth floor was making these, and radar was a memory.

At the outset, the Signal Corps had specified that radar being a very secret project, all prints and information must be guarded with extreme caution. It directed that prints must be signed for by one designated person who would be responsible for them and to whom they must be returned before the end of a shift. Later, the Corps ruled that only such prints as related to certain details of the antenna mount must be treated as secret. When Chrysler Engineering designed the semi-trailer, the prints, for secrecy's sake, showed what appeared to be a searchlight reflector protruding from the roof where the paraboloid would function.

Few of the thousands who worked at Dodge ever passed the doors of the radar shop. Carl Norden's famous bomb sight, guarded as it was, was known by name to every newspaper reader, but the word "radar" was not spoken for a long time. The prudent

Girl assembling the 48 slip rings on the radar's main drive shaft.

did not ask what was going on in the old quarters of the Engineering section at Dodge; the imprudent were told that it was a "Signal Corps job."

It had taken seven trucks to house and carry the 268 radar, pre-war prototype of the SCR-584. So compact is the SCR-584 antenna mount as designed by Chrysler Engineering that it and its accompanying electronic apparatus are housed in a 19½-foot semi-trailer, small enough to clear the hatches of a Victory ship. Chrysler Engineering also designed the trailer, but the Dodge Truck plant, which normally would have made it, was too busy with military vehicle orders and this job was sub-let to Fruehauf, a specialist in this field.

*Attaching the co-axial cable to the electrical heart
of the SCR-584 radar before the first of many tests.*

Moving along the highway to Syracuse or Baltimore it might have passed for a furniture van, except
for its olive drab paint and the armed guard which
accompanied each, but it had a rigidity and strength
far beyond anything expected of a commercial truck.

The paraboloid reflector is raised through a trap
door in the roof when put into use. Being a precision
measuring device, the least flutter in the trailer body
would be as fatal to accuracy in the dish as if a high-
powered telescope were mounted on a wobbly base.
As the mount also must be exactly level for accuracy,

the trailer body may be canted into plumb from any position by a series of built-in jacks.

* * * * *

The discovery of radar appears to date, as nearly as any invention may be pinned down to an exact time, from a September afternoon in 1922 when two research engineers in the Naval Aircraft Laboratory at Anacostia, across the creek from Washington, first noted that radio signals were reflected from steel buildings and other large metal objects.

Looking closer into this phenomenon, they found that ships passing up and down the Potomac set up an interference pattern in radio sending and receiving. The two young men were Dr. A. Hoyt Taylor and Leo C. Young, the former now chief consultant and coordinator for electronics of the Naval Research Laboratory, the latter his first assistant.

This gave them an idea: maybe this phenomenon could be harnessed in a way to detect the passage of an enemy vessel in darkness, fog or smoke screen between any two destroyers in extended line. They sent a report of their discovery and its possible uses to the Navy's Bureau of Engineering on September 27, 1922, and were encouraged to pursue this idea along with other research problems sent them.

Taylor and Hoyt had not discovered radio reflection; that had been noted as a curiosity as far back as 1887 by Henrich Hertz, the great German physicist and pioneer in electronics, but the subject had not been pursued. In World War I, both sides soon learned how to locate the other's radio stations by triangulation, a principle soon adopted to marine navigation, vessels at sea getting their position by triangulation of their radio signals from two shore stations, a simple geometric equation.

Not so long after this, radio amateurs of the crystal set period began to be aware that on waves as long as 20 meters, often at 10 meters, an airplane passing overhead would deflect their signals; and in the 30's the commercial air lines began to adopt this principle as an altimeter. By measuring the elapsed time between the sending of a beamed signal from a plane and its rebound from the earth, the plane's altitude, not above sea level, but above the immediate ground below, could be determined accurately in the worst of visibility.

The electrical insides of the radar main shaft are visible in this scene on the Dodge assembly line.

Final test booth for the azimuth gearing. Electrical Engineer Sachse and Electrical Inspector Danielson at work.

The British admit that they first discovered the practical military application of radio reflection from reports of our Naval Research Laboratory and of the Carnegie Institution published between 1926 and

1930. It is possible that the Axis discovered radar's war uses from the same source, though both the Germans and the Japanese long had been experimenting with radio reflection.

The Japanese physicist, Hidetsugo Yagi, was so famous in this field that our Navy called its early radar antennae "yagis." Thereafter, each nation worked out the military application independently up to 1940 when, even before our entry into the war, the United States and Great Britain began the free exchange of radar data. Under the stimulus of war, the British were well ahead of us on airborne radar and, no doubt, the Germans were, too.

To return to the 1920's, eight years of experimentation went on before, in November, 1930, Dr. Taylor submitted a report on "radio echo signals from moving objects" which led the Navy's Bureau of Engineering to assign to the research laboratory this specific problem: "Investigate the use of radio to detect the presence of enemy vessels and aircraft; special emphasis is placed upon the confidential nature of this problem."

The following January the Secretary of the Navy wrote the Secretary of War describing these experiments and making this suggestion: "Certain phases of the problem appear to be of more concern to the Army than to the Navy. For example, a system of transmitters and receivers might be set up about a defense area to test their effectiveness in detecting the passage of hostile aircraft into the area."

By 1931 planes at a distance of 50 miles had been spotted by radio reflection under favorable circumstances and Dr. Taylor, reporting this fact, added that the laboratory's object now must be to "develop instruments for the collection, automatic recording and correlating of data to show the position, angle and speed of approach of plane or ship." This was the true crossing of the frontier from observed phenomena into practical use, and the real inception of what we now call radar. Hence it is about 15 years old.

So much progress was made in the next four years

The radar pedestal gets a coat of Army olive drab via spray gun in a paint booth.

in developing such automatic instruments that the House Naval Appropriations Committee, excited by what it was told in 1935, voluntarily gave the Naval Research Laboratory a special appropriation of $100,000 with which to pursue this research.

A demonstration in June, 1936, of the steadily improving apparatus made an enthusiastic convert of Admiral Bowen, chief of the Bureau of Engineering, who ordered a set installed experimentally on a battleship as an adjunct to gun fire control. Tested in the Pacific fleet maneuvers that fall, it converted the Navy's line officers. The next two years were given to producing a practical shipboard model installed late in 1939 on the battleship *New York* and exhaustively tested in battle maneuvers in January, February and March, 1940. This was the first permanent American radar installation.

Production manufacture of radar had begun in October, 1939 with the letting of a contract to the Radio Corporation for six sets like that on the *USS New York*. Two of the major electronics laboratories of America, those of Bell Telephone and RCA, by then were working closely with the Naval Research Laboratory. The next August, Admiral Bowen persuaded General Electric to enter the new field. It did so so whole-heartedly that it transferred its large staff of radio research engineers without exception to radar.

General Electric was given a naval contract and a month or so later Westinghouse had been enlisted, so that nearly all of our battleships and heavy cruisers had been equipped before Pearl Harbor and early warning radar sets had been installed on our strategic frontiers.

When the war began our Army was using the 268 mobile radar set for anti-aircraft gun-laying, operating on a wave length of $1\frac{1}{2}$ meters, common to all the warring nations and then thought of as short wave. The 268 had replaced in 1939 a complicated and inaccurate system of sound locators, searchlights, opti-

Bolting the radar base to the elevator platform on which the instrument will rest when installed in the trailer.

cal range finders and tracking telescopes. The SCR-584 microwave set which replaced the 268, in turn, and other new type radars, were the creations of the Radiation Laboratory set up in 1940 at the Massachusetts Institute of Technology by the National Research Defense Committee, an independent agency established by executive order that year to "correlate and support scientific research on the mechanisms and devices of warfare."

The Radiation Laboratory, a civilian body operating in close cooperation with the Services, but independently of military authority, its spending supervised only by NDRC, began with a personnel of 48 housed in a few rooms and grew to a force of 3,900 men and women, including probably 20% of the nation's top physicists, using 660,380 square feet of space.

Though 268 doctors of philosophy and one Nobel prize winner served on the staff, the average age of the thousand odd scientists it recruited was 32 years. The Laboratory spent up to July 31, 1945, for nothing but radar research and development, $80,000,000, or nearly twice the endowment of M.I.T. itself. The Army and Navy contracted with private manufacturers for more than two-and-a-half billion dollars of radar equipment based directly upon Radiation Laboratory developments.

The Laboratory had branches in England, Hawaii, Manila and on the Mediterranean, all connected by teletype with Cambridge; sent its scientific personnel

The experimental antenna mount, replaced by the Chrysler design, was too heavy and cumbersome.

into the field, the South Pacific included, under fire to study this equipment in action and to counsel the operating forces. It has been estimated that "RL" in five years advanced radar research by at least 25 normal peacetime years.

Though no microwave equipment was delivered to Army or Navy in 1941 and very little in 1942, almost all Allied radar equipment by 1944 was based upon microwave technics that had been no more than a speculative possibility three years earlier.

In the midst of the great air blitz of Britain in the summer of 1940 a British mission came to the United States seeking to learn what we were doing in radar. Ordinary vacuum tubes were adequate to the 1½ meter radar which defeated the Luftwaffe that summer. The greater accuracy of microwaves was known, but they demanded, among other technical advances, tubes of a power many hundred times that of anything known in this frequency range.

Dr. Vannevar Bush, then head of NDRC, appointed Dr. Compton to set up a special section of NDRC at M.I.T. to develop detection devices of all kinds. A Microwave Radar Committee appointed by Dr. Compton decided that the problem was so important that it called for a laboratory of its own with wide powers and a large staff. Dr. Lee DuBridge, now President of The California Institute of Technology, was borrowed from the University of Rochester as director of this Radiation Laboratory.

The British Admiralty had put the problem of a greatly more powerful vacuum tube up to a research group at the University of Birmingham who had developed the revolutionary cavity magnetron with a million times more power. The British left samples of the cavity magnetron with the new Radiation Laboratory and suggested that it concentrate upon two problems: (1) a microwave radar for use in and with night fighter planes for the interception of hostile aircraft, and (2) a microwave radar that could follow enemy planes with sufficient accuracy to permit effective blind anti-aircraft fire. As yet unaware that they had won the "Battle of Britain" against the Luftwaffe, the British were concerned with little else.

Even with the great advance gained by the cavity magnetron, many competent men doubted at the

Roof test at Dodge where the instruments were run thousands of hours without use of high frequency current.

time that microwaves could be adapted to radar. Others thought that it could be done, but not done fast enough to play a part in the war.

The Radiation Laboratory quickly perfected a night fighter microwave radar, however, and early in its testing it was found to have many unsuspected advantages over previously known sets in spotting ships on the surface of the sea. Out of this discovery came the sea-search radar which accounted for more than half the U-boats sunk after mid-1942.

In the early stages of the war most German subs were lost when they surfaced at night to recharge their batteries and were detected by British 1½ meter airborne and naval radar. The Nazis defeated this radar with radar detectors, which warned the surfaced U-boat of a plane's proximity.

In 1942 the Germans were sinking Allied shipping at the rate of 16,000 tons a day. This grave peril was nearly eliminated within a few weeks by microwave radar which drove the Nazis to devise the Schnorkel, a breathing tube through which air was conducted to the engines and foul air exhausted without surfacing.

A further improvement of the sea-search set then achieved a perfection which would spot even the Schnorkel or the thin periscope of a submerged sub. In the latter stages of the war Hitler sent two parties of civilian electronics experts to sea in U-boats with orders to find a way of combatting this newest Allied radar. One of these submarines survived thirteen

Phantom drawing showing the mechanism of the spinner motor and the antenna which it spins at 1750 times a minute.

days, the other nine, and Hitler virtually abandoned the U-boat campaign.

Before turning to this adaptation of the night fighter radar, the Laboratory had begun work on its second assignment out of which came its crowning achievement, the SCR-584 anti-aircraft set. If you recall news reels of anti-aircraft fire you will remember that, as a rule, you have seen the whole sky dotted with black bursts, many of them not remotely on the target, an indication of the relative inaccuracy of long wave radar-controlled guns. In a news reel of SCR-584-directed gun fire you discover the hostile plane by looking for the bursts which march directly in front of or behind or on the target.

A few RAF planes were able to stop the many of the Luftwaffe over Britain because the British radio-locator, as they called their long wave radar, spotted the enemy as they took off from fields across the Channel. This enabled ground-directed RAF fighters to be upstairs and waiting for the Luftwaffe at the right points at the right times. When the RAF smashed 185 of the then record-breaking flight of 500 Nazi bombers which attacked England September 15, 1940, the Germans abandoned mass daylight for night attacks, only to discover the British just as well prepared in the dark, thanks to radar.

When they learned what was tipping their hands, the Germans took to flying over the Channel a few feet above the water. The meter and a half wave was

Detroit calls this a "fixture." A fixture is anything which holds work in fixed position during machining or assembly.

undependable at low elevations, particularly over water. While water is a better reflector than is the earth, its surface is so flat that the beams tend to ricochet off it, leaving a margin at the water line where planes might slip through undetected by radar. This German practice became so general that Allied pilots were instructed never to return across the Channel at less than 1,000 feet, and any plane crossing West at less than this altitude was fired upon at sight.

The Germans were on the defensive and an enemy plane seldom ventured over England by the time the first 132 sets of the SCR-584 radar reached Britain as

Final touches on the semi-trailers before installation of radar sets.

part of the invasion equipment of the army General Eisenhower was assembling there. But even before Christmas of 1943 the British Intelligence had warned the Government to expect Hitler's secret weapon, the V-1 buzz bomb at any time.

The British and American invasion armies and all the vast stores of supplies accumulated for them had to be protected, as well as the civil population, against this new threat, and so most of the SCR-584's soon were deployed along the Channel coast in the hope of intercepting these small and very fast robot bombs which, even with radar, gave a maximum warning of only three minutes between the alert and the opening of fire.

Before the capture of the original launching sites which finally stopped the V-1 bombs over England six weeks after the attack began, Hitler already had lost faith in this no longer secret weapon, only 10% of which were penetrating the radar-directed defense, and had turned to his final card, the V-2. But when the Germans had been driven from France and coastal Belgium they concentrated their V-1 fire on Antwerp in an effort to prevent Allied use of that great port. Here the buzz bomb defense was exclusively by radar-directed guns and two SCR-584 sets were partly destroyed by the bombs.

When our 8th Air Force began to pioneer daylight pin-point bombing over North Europe the Luftwaffe still was a formidable force, and German radar was good and German flak wicked. Nevertheless, the 8th found that its No. 1 problem was not the enemy but just plain navigation to the target and back. In the weather which prevails from November through March over North Europe they did well to grope their way home, let alone to find a designated target from 20,000 feet and hit it.

Just twelve of a new microwave airborne radar set hastily produced by the Radiation Laboratory, however, multiplied the winter effectiveness of our strategic bombers ten to twenty times. The British christened them "Mickeys." Twelve were all that could be given the 8th, that most important winter, yet

Each semi-trailer was put through a high pressure shower bath to test the tightness of its joints against rain.

one squadron of "Mickey"-equipped planes could lead sixty times their number on a raid, getting them up through the soup, guiding them direct to the target, telling them when to drop their bombs and getting them home again—so far as navigation hazards were concerned. The first such raid was on

Wilhelmshaven which eight earlier visual raids had missed. They hit it on the button through a heavy overcast.

By the next winter all American and British strategic bombers were "Mickey"-equipped. But there were other planes, the tactical aircraft. They are fast, small, short-ranged, 1-place fighter-bombers and strafers. One of their duties is systematically to harass enemy ground forces and reduce their positions in close liaison with our ground forces, brief missions calling for speedy action and a minimum of briefing. We had an increasing surplus of such planes as the Luftwaffe declined, giving our fighters less and less to do in good weather. In bad weather, they were grounded.

In good weather, an Air Force observer sits up front, in possibly a tank, and radio-telephones a plane flying over to look for a camouflaged gun position which the ground forces have not been able to locate closely enough to knock it out with counter fire, or to warn of a column of enemy armor spotted in the distance. The pilot locates the target and dive bombs or machine guns it.

But in bad weather the tactical aircraft pilot, swooshing over at tremendous speeds, either can not see the ground or sees it so hazily that his support may be worse than his enmity. Because he is likely to bomb or strafe his own infantry or artillery, he is pulled out, leaving the poor foot soldier stuck in the mud without air support.

Phantom view of the SCR-584 Radar unit and trailer.

A radar set would be an awkward addition to the cockpit of a single-place plane. More important, the pilot of such a fast plane has no time for the study of a radar scope. But by a brilliant adaptation of the SCR-584, the Radiation Laboratory gave the tactical aircraft eyes to see through the dark or the weather.

The Laboratory reasoned that if the SCR-584 could find the position of a plane and plot its track accurately enough to enable guns five miles below to fire shells to the point in space which the plane would reach twenty seconds later, then a controller on the ground, using the SCR-584, should be able to guide a plane to exactly the spot in space which is correct for the blind release of bombs to hit an unseen target, or the right spot in space for the beginning of a dive-bombing attack on a target which the pilot isn't able to see when he begins his dive.

By this new technic of warfare which we called Close Support, fighter-bombers and photographic reconnaissance planes were pointed to their targets from ground radar plotting rooms. There an electronically-moved pen traced the ground course of a plane across a military grid map. Radar pulses echoing back from the plane were tied in with an electromechanical plotting board with a glass surface illuminated from below, a 1/250,000 scale map laid over the glass, a sheet of tracing paper laid over the map. Vacuum tubes translated the radar echo's report to

The SCR-584 radar as made by Chrysler undergoing its final test for backlash in the elevation and azimuth gear trains.

a servo mechanism which drove the pen.

As the target was neared, the large map was replaced by an 800-yards-to-the-inch scale map of the immediate target area. In effect, the SCR-584 controller in the plotting room of the Fighter Control Center saw the plane or flight of planes approach the target much as an airplane pilot might see an automobile below him approaching a town.

In the big strategic bombers the target would be sighted through the clouds by airborne radar and the bomb drop made by the Norden bomb sight which computes the altitude, the speed of the plane, gravity pull of the bomb and deflection of the wind. In Close Support all this is done by remote control in the plotting room, the altitude, speed, gravity and deflection added algebraically to the map parallaxes of the target, as corrected for the curvature of the earth. The Norden bomb sight often was used in the plotting room, though only for the computation.

Radiation Laboratory physicists made the first plotting tables by hand at the Laboratory's British branch at Great Malvern of such parts as they could pick up in England plus what could be rushed to them from home by plane. Production models were made later by the Bell Telephone Laboratory though not in time to reach Europe before the war's end. A field modification set designed by the Radiation Laboratory extended the SCR-584's range to 50

The Chrysler-built radar unit in place inside the 10-ton semi-trailer which housed it and accessory apparatus.

miles for Close Support liaison, even to 100 miles if the plane was equipped with a responder beacon.

Close Support first was used in July, 1944, to direct three P-47's on a flight to dive-bomb visually a bridge behind the German lines obscured by overcast. The SCR-584 sent them over the target at 9,000 feet, directed them into a 90 degree turn, then into a

When put into use, the SCR-584 radar is raised through a trap door. Side panels are opened to show the process.

45 degree angle dive which brought them through the clouds directly over the target. Communication between the controller and the pilot is by very high frequency radiophone.

Similarly, it enabled the direction of photographic planes by night or in daylight under weather which had until now prevented the taking of mosaic photographs. Suppose that the ground forces wish a set of mosaic pictures taken by night of a highway behind the enemy lines when the traffic on it will be densest. The controller directs the pilot on a course parallel to and immediately over the road, tells him when to drop his flares to illuminate it for his camera.

In the battle of the Bulge the only planes able to take the air in the first few days of near zero visibility were SCR-584-directed tactical planes. Major General Elwood Quesada, commanding the 9th Tactical Air Force, said of that battle in an official report: "Radar's work during the period of the German break through was outstanding. The Bulge contained no well-defined topographic features. The whole thing could be flown around in less than ten minutes. Roads were chockablock with movement. From the air we couldn't distinguish our vehicles from theirs. (One reason was that snow had blotted out identification marks.) It is our hope to track by radar each flight directed into the Bulge. The number of American lives saved by our ability to stop attacks on our own columns and installations can not be measured; nor can we measure the number of Germans killed because our fighter-bomber boys can be informed with assurance that other columns are enemy."

In other words, knowing pretty well where our own forces in the Bulge were, and knowing exactly, by means of radar, where each of our fighter-bombers was at any moment, the control room was able to tell a pilot whether the column below him was our own or German.

As might be expected of a people of their technological skill, the German radar was excellent, though they had neither the PPI scope, the IFF identification nor the unjammable microwave. Between Cap de la Hague on Cherbourg peninsula and the Dutch border they had as of D-Day 75 major radar installations just behind the coast. This, of course, did not include such mobile radars as the Wurzburg set supplied every four heavy anti-aircraft guns. A necessary preliminary to D-Day was the destruction or temporary disabling by rockets, bombs and strafing of each of these major radar stations—and only one

Close-up of a radar mechanism in position for scanning on the roof of its rolling home.

survived within gun range of the beaches chosen for the Allied landings.

This, however, did not so much account for the failure of a single German fighter to intercept the 844 transport planes and 105 gliders which dropped or landed 15,000 airborne troops behind the beaches

The semi-trailer radar housing was designed by Chrysler but made by the Fruehauf Company, as sub-contractor.

on D-Day as did an elaborate ruse. On the left flank of the invasion area heavy British plane concentrations with radar jamming equipment, and dropping dummy parachutists, decoyed a great part of the German fighter strength into the Dover-Calais area the night before. These Luftwaffe planes spent most of the night circling there. Similar diversionary feints on the right flank, each using jamming equipment which simulated on the German radar full airborne invasions, pulled much of the rest of the German fighters into the region East of Cap d-Antifer. With the German backfield lured to each side, the invasion bored through the center.

How do you jam radar? There are two known ways. One is by beamed interference, as radio is jammed, an electronic raspberry, so to speak. As a rule, two planes of every flight were equipped with three transmitters each tuned to the wave length of the enemy's radar. The British often put mikes on their aircraft engines and transmitted their roar as an all-effacing Bronx cheer. The Allied code name for this form of jamming was "carpet." Birds in flight were killed and cooked almost instantly when they crossed the path of high-powered radar-jamming ground stations.

"Window" was the code name of the second form, though the British usually spoke of it as "chaff." This employed quantities of tin foil strips fed out of a tube. These strips were light enough to float long in the upper air and, being metallic coated, radar pulses echoed back from them, hopelessly confusing long wave sets. One chaff-equipped plane could convince all but microwave radar that the sky was full of hostiles.

The Germans were using chaff as early as February, 1942, when it enabled the battleships *Scharnhorst* and *Gneisnau* to make their escape up the Channel from a French port where they were supposedly bottled-up. Though every square foot of the Channel was watched by radar, a shower of tinfoil strips and a barrage of beamed static blinded the

Completed job moving to the drive-away line. Here the radar unit has been elevated to the roof for photographic purposes.

British sets. The British first used chaff July 24, 1943, in a 2,000 plane attack on Hamburg, the heaviest of the war until then. How well the Germans kept their military secrets from the civil populace was demonstrated by the reaction of the people in the Hamburg vicinity who believed the falling foil to be some new form of poison attack.

Ground Control Approach, or GCA, was another microwave development of the Radiation Laboratory. This unit operating in an 11-ton truck landed twenty B-29's on Iwo Jima on one day of particularly filthy weather, bombers returning from Japanese raids which almost certainly would have been lost otherwise.

This set included two distinct radar systems. With

one, the operators search on the PPI scope the air surrounding a field, directing plane traffic approaching from all directions into the sector scanned by the second system. The latter, a high-precision short range radar, giving practically continuous information on the unseen plane's position, is used by the final controller to guide the pilot down the glidepath. One precision indicator shows the height of the plane and of all ground obstacles along the path; the other shows the plane's lateral position with respect to the runway.

These replaced beam systems by which pilots land on instruments in the plane, demanding special installations in the plane, considerable ground equipment and rigorous training of the pilots.

A letter from a Radiation Laboratory engineer assisting in the introduction of the Army's first GCA

set, near Verdun, reported: "Two P-61's returning from a night mission were caught up in the soup. The ceiling was essentially zero and so was the visibility. The first P-61 came in right on the button the first time. They asked him when he had seen the runway and his now-famous answer was 'I didn't. I just felt a bump.'

"The second P-61 was off in azimuth on the first run so they told him he'd have to go around again. He came back with: 'You'll have to make it quick or I won't have enough gas to go high enough to bail out.'

"They brought him around in a very tight pattern and this time he touched down though he couldn't see more than one runway light at a time. When he stopped rolling he had twenty gallons of gas left which, for the 2,000-hp. engine in a P-61 is just about one

Drive-away line of mobile radars about to leave Dodge plant under armed guard for Syracuse and Baltimore.

good cough. A major told us that really made GCA part of the outfit from then on."

Another form of radar, the long-range or early-warning detector, first was put to use at Panama on October 7, 1940, and the next day picked up a Pan-American transport from Miami when it was 118 miles away. These long-range sets were shipped out on high priority as fast as they could be manufactured to the most dangerous points.

They should not be confused with the long range navigation system called Loran by which a ship or a plane at distances up to 1,000 miles from a "radio light house" can accurately locate itself. Loran is not properly radar because its pulses are non-directional and because they are received and amplified at the ship rather than being reflected automatically. Loran uses long waves and, therefore, its beam is trapped by the ionosphere and follows the curvature of the earth just as commercial radio waves do.

Nor does the radar principle account for the precision flight of bats, as has been stated in the newspapers. In flight, the darting bat emits a constant stream of cries pitched at 50,000 cycles or beyond, far above the limits of the human ear. This continuous squeaking is reflected back from branches, wires, walls and all obstructions. It is supersonic radiation, a phenomenon of sound, not of electronics.

When Theodore Roosevelt sent the fleet around the world in 1907 the ship which could drop a shell upon

a stationary target the size of an ordinary hull at 4,000 yards or a little more than two miles could paint an E for excellent on its gun turrets. Even in World War I fleets still fought on visual contact and admirals jockied and feinted in an effort to maneuver the enemy "up sun"—that is, with the sun in his eyes. Firing ceased with dark.

Ranges beyond twelve miles were of little value except for shelling fixed shore installations, unless supplemented by aircraft reconnaissance information, until the advent of radar which enables a warship to "see" electronically and hit a moving target on the remote horizon or hidden by night, fog or smoke screen, as we repeatedly found and punished the Jap Navy when there still was a Jap Navy. In a modern naval battle, the Admiral on the bridge may never catch a glimpse of the enemy he has engaged, but that enemy is visible to his subordinates below decks in the Combat Information Room, made so by radar.

The Bismarck destroyed the great Hood with her second salvo at 23,000 yards or more than 13 miles and was hunted down in turn by radar. An American battleship's 16-inch guns hit the Jean Bart at Casablanca with her first salvo at 26,000 yards, put the French battleship out of action with her second salvo.

Radar first made it possible to cruise and fight in fleet formation at night under a total blackout, eliminating all danger of collision. Early in the war a formation of cruisers was ordered to bombard by night

Whatever the short-wave radar beam discovers appears as a recognizable image on the face of this cathode ray electronic tube.

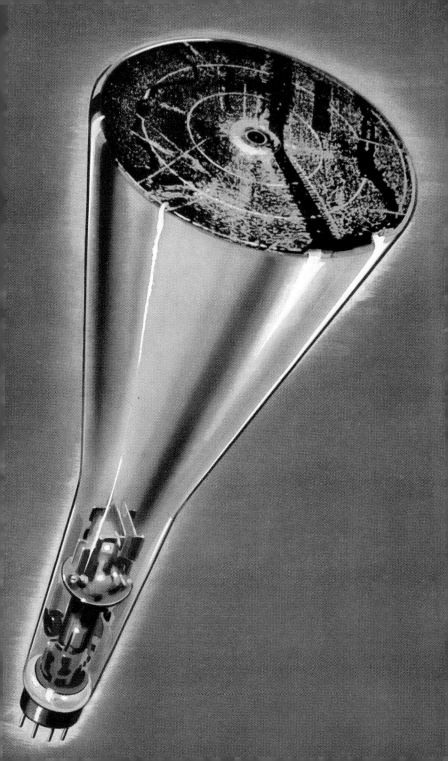

a Jap stronghold from close in. These waters were reef strewn and never had been charted accurately— except by the Japanese. Yet blacked-out on the darkest of nights, the cruisers steamed in formation at 30 miles an hour, avoiding several mine-sweepers in their path, went straight to the unseen mark, blasted it, returned without a scratch on any hull and reported that one reef was six miles out of its true position on their charts. The eyes of radar did it all.

Radar, of course, accompanied our forces at every step on our island hops from Australia toward Japan. For the first few weeks after each new landing, the SCR-584 radar and its anti-aircraft guns were the front line of defense. Ships had to be discharged, depots, hospitals, bivouac areas and headquarters set up and protected from sneak attacks by night from Jap aircraft, of which a troublesome number always remained in the vicinity for a while.

Japan's over-extended empire came apart through lack of shipping. One 14th Air Force group flying B-24's from a field many hundred miles inland in China sank 110,000 tons of Japanese shipping in the China Sea in one month entirely by night and by radar direction. That presumably was why the Japs in the last weeks of the war made such a drive in force against our forward air bases at Liuchow and Kweilin.

Such a little way has man penetrated into the unknown world of electronics that it is easily possible that today's microwave radar will seem as crude

Plotting board for "close control" of tactical aircraft set up inside an SCR-584 radar truck.

as a 1921 crystal radio set alongside tomorrow's all-seeing eye; and that these military applications are the least of its potential magic.

Already we know that it is a post-war necessity of all sea and air traffic. The Maritime Commission has ordered it installed on all our merchant ships. A ship so equipped will be forewarned of any obstruction to navigation whether land, iceberg, derelict, exposed reef or another vessel. Radar-equipped planes will have a constant visual picture in any weather and by night of the ground beneath and ahead, will be forewarned of other planes, of mountains; can land in emergencies anywhere the pilot could sit down on a clear day; will be guided by radar in and out of fields, navigated by it to their destinations. The mapping of the moon by radar short waves has been forecast by the English physicist, Sir Edward Appleton.

As radar rewrote the rule books of war, so it has given man a sixth sense whereby almost any fantasy seems possible.

When the Radiation Laboratory was disbanding in October, 1945, Dr. Getting wrote to Mr. Keller: "Those of us who have worked so closely with you and your engineers feel particularly sad that the closing of our Laboratory will also mean

the end of this close association with you. I can honestly say that nowhere during the past five years have I met with a more efficiently administered engineering laboratory or a finer group of fellows than at the Chrysler Corporation."

Dr. DuBridge, director of the Laboratory, wrote a few days later: "No company has cooperated with us in a more patriotic and self-effacing way than the Chrysler Corporation. I have been deeply impressed by the efficiency and speed and ability of both your engineering and your manufacturing people. I am certain that the SCR-584 anti-aircraft radars would not have been completed in time or designed with such reliability had not your group played such an important role."

The Corporation treasures such praise for a war product which it designed and built from scratch.

South Seas radar information pool, First Island Command, Noumea. 53 radar posts are listed on the blackboard.